Another Load of IF...

By the same author
Maggie's Farm (Penguin)
Further Down on Maggie's Farm (Penguin)
The If . . . Chronicles (Methuen)
If . . . Only Again (Methuen)

Another Load of IF...

Steve Bell

Methuen

A METHUEN PAPERBACK

This collection first published in 1985
by Methuen London Ltd
11 New Fetter Lane, London EC4P 4EE
Reprinted 1986

The strips first published by *The Guardian* 1984 and 1985

Copyright © Steve Bell 1984, 1985

Designed by Brian Homer
Edited by Steve Bell and Brian Homer

Typeset by P & W Typesetters
202 Hagley Road, Edgbaston, Birmingham

Made and printed in Great Britain
by Richard Clay (The Chaucer Press) Ltd
Bungay, Suffolk

ISBN 0 413 58670 7

For Heather, William and Joe

Your Stars

by Russell Orsiz World's only Cowboy Astrologer

Howdy Starpards!

I was readin' my breakfast plate this mornin' and the bean stains said to me:
"Russell you ol' son of a gun, you're gonna fart like fury before this mornin's out!"
It was right, I did. It always is, I always do.

When I was asked to come up with some predictions for the coming political year, I decided to make some general political predictions, and then, sign by sign to make some personal predictions you may all find relevant and useful.

Here are my general predictions for 1986:
Some senior Members of the House of Lords will pass on to another world.
The Prime Minister will go on an important foreign visit.
There may be a Royal Happy Event.
There will be controversy over government economic policy.
A dead rat will be thrown at the Pope (or was that last year?)

All in all a pretty busy and interesting twelve months.

Yippeeyiyay, Starpards!

Russell Orsiz

5

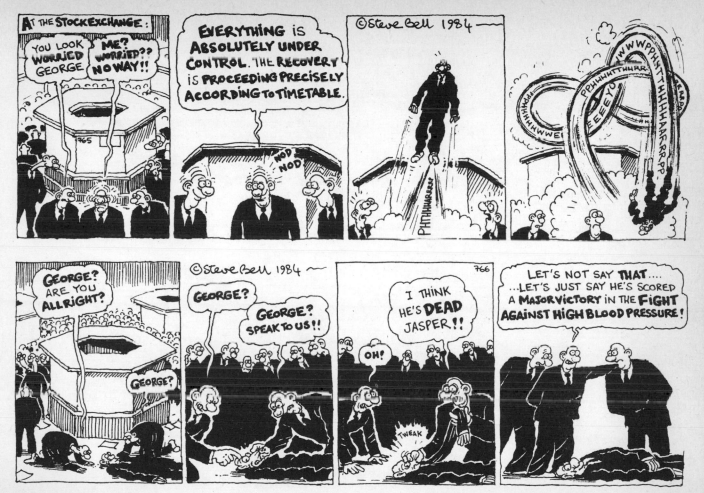

7

8

9

10

12

CANCER
June 21st-July 20th

Cancerians do have a tendency to nip around sideways. There may be some hot days this month when some of you will have to remove items of clothing. Be careful to wash your genitals thoroughly.

Some well known Cancerians
William Whitelaw
Edward Heath
Cyril Smith
Doctor Death
The Prince & Princess of Wales

HOW FARE MY BLUE BOYS, MARSHAL FATS?
WE NEED REINFORCEMENTS MA'AM, BUT THEY'RE ALREADY COSTING A PACKET
©Steve Bell '84
THEN WE MUST SEND IN MY KHAKI BOYS TOOTSWEET!
BUT MA'AM... THE KHAKI BOYS ARE ALREADY IN THERE...
777.
....DRESSED UP AS BLUE BOYS!!
WHAT?! YOU MEAN WE'RE RUNNING OUT OF BLUE BOYS AND KHAKI BOYS?
GOOD DAY MADAME L'EMPEREUR – AND HOW WOULD YOU SAY THE WAR IS GOING??
WAR? WHAT WAR? NOTHING TO DO WITH MOI!

HOW CAN YOU TELL THE DIFFERENCE BETWEEN COPPERS AND SOLDIERS DRESSED UP AS COPPERS?
OH THAT'S EASY...
© Steve Bell 1984
...YOU CAN ALWAYS TELL THE SQUADDIES BECAUSE THEY'RE THE ONES WHO COULDN'T FIND HELMETS SMALL ENOUGH..
..BUT THE CLINCHER IS WHEN THEY'VE DONE A TOUR IN THE FALKLANDS..
778.
...IT ALWAYS SHOWS UP IN THEIR CONVERSATION
WHAT WOULDN'T I GIVE FOR A NICE MUNCH OF GRASS AND GUANO!
BAAAAAA

15

17

19

20

NOW DOWN TO BUSINESS. TO BECOME A HIGH COURT JUDGE UNDER NORMAL CIRCUMSTANCES TAKES ABOUT **FORTY YEARS.** WE HAVE **DISTILLED** THAT TRAINING INTO A **FIVE DAY SCHEME**.....

793.

...NOW, ON **DAY ONE**, FIRST THINGS FIRST, WE HAVE **THE DINNERS. THIRTY SIX DINNERS IN ALL**, AND I'D LIKE YOU TO **EAT THEM ALL BY 6 O'CLOCK** THIS EVENING....

G.G.GORDON B.B.BENNETT!!

© Steve Bell 1984

AND SO: VERY WELL DONE MR. KIPLING! NOW YOU'VE EATEN THE **DINNERS** WE TURN TO THE **DRINK.** ON AVERAGE WE HAVE CALCULATED YOU MUST CONSUME **ONE BOTTLE** OF **PORT** OR **SHERRY** AND **TWO BOTTLES** OF **CLARET EVERY DAY** FOR **FORTY YEARS.**

AWNWWNNGG BWORP

...THAT COMES TO APPROXIM-ATELY **4,800 GALLONS** OF **CLARET** AND **2,400 GALLONS** OF **SHERRY**, WHICH WE COULDN'T POSSIBLY EXPECT YOU TO DRINK IN **FIVE DAYS.** HOWEVER, THE LORD CHANCELLOR **HAS** GRANTED A **SPECIAL DISPENS-ATION** FOR YOU TO **SOAK IN A TANK** CONTAINING THE AFORESAID AMOUNTS OF REFRESHMENT FOR **12 HOURS.** SEE YOU IN THE MORNING.

HONK

* THANKS TO PETE F.

YOU'RE **DOING WELL**, MR. KIPLING — YOU'VE **EATEN** THE **DINNERS** AND YOU'VE **SOAKED UP** THE **CLARET** AND THE **SHERRY**, THIS MORNING WE **PREPARE YOU INTELLECTUALLY** TO BECOME A **HIGH COURT JUDGE**...

© Steve Bell 1984

...DURING THE **NORMAL 40 YEAR COURSE** OF TRAINING, A **JUDGE** WOULD EXPECT TO READ ABOUT **12,400 COPIES** OF THE **TIMES** AND AN **EQUAL NUMBER** OF **DAILY TELEGRAPHS.** NOW WITH THE AID OF **MODERN TECHNOLOGY**....

...WE'VE MANAGED TO **BOIL DOWN** THAT ACCUMUL-ATION OF **KNOWLEDGE** AND **WISDOM** INTO **ONE SMALL PILL!**

NNNGG

YOU'LL FEEL **PRETTY UNUSUAL** FOR A WHILE

GNH! MY HEAD! IT'S EXPLODING!

RUMBLE

...AND **NOW** YOU UNDERSTAND WHY **JUDGES** WEAR **FUNNY WIGS** — IT'S TO **STOP THEIR HEADS BLOW-ING OFF!!**

794

HARRUMPH HARRUMPH HARRUMPH

LEO
July 21st-August 21st

You enjoy eating large meals and lying around up trees. Some of you may go on holiday this month.

Watch out for people carrying chairs.

Some well known Leos
Michael Foot
The Queen Mother

25

28

29

807.

808.

30

In the land of spent banana in a village by a deep hole lived a Nottinghamshire miner and his name was **SILVER LARCH**...

SPECIAL THANKS TO HEATHER   813

To the land of spent banana far across the great wide water at the call of **Margaret Thatcher**

Margaret Thatcher Grocer's Daughter came **Macgregor** hatchet man...

Silver Larch loved **Minnie Miner** in the land of spent banana wanted them to work together, in the pay of **Ian Macgregor Ian Macgregor Coal Board Chairman** in the deep hole for a pittance at the **Grocer's Daughter's** pleasure,...

For as long as she should hold them economically viable till they could lie down together he and Minnie on the scrapheap on the economic scrapheap

"You are off your head!" she told him...

"Now I know why they all call you 'Silver Larch'" said Minnie Miner. "Why is that then?" Silver Larch asked. "You are thick as plank" she said.

Silver Larch met **Daily Mailman** in the land of spent banana said he was sincerely worried by the miners leftward lurching

Arthur Scargill Miners' Leader filled **Mailman** and **'Larch'** with terror terror that his awesome hairstyle was a vile intimidation....

Daily Mailman wrote a leader criticising **Scargill's hairstyle** said that if the striking miners won their fight then everybody would be forced to have their haircut in the style of **Arthur Scargill**....

As it was in grip of **Red Bear** as it was in Eastern Europe 'neath the rumbling Russian armour

Vidal Sassoon outlawed there.

814.

33

MEANWHILE IN THE SOUTH WALES VALLEYS MILLIONAIRES WERE MAKING MONEY SHIFTING CHINESE COAL IN LORRIES MAKING VAST AMOUNTS OF MONEY....

STRIKING MINERS SAID: "YOU MUSTN'T!" TILL A HIGH COURT JUDGE DECIDED MINERS WERE HENCEFORTH ILLEGAL MINERS NOW HAD TO BE POODLES STAY AT WORK AND BRING HOME BOODLE...

SLAPPED A HEAVY FINE UPON THEM MINERS SAID: "WE WILL NOT PAY HIM!" BARRICADED UP THEIR WIGWAM CALLED THE JUSTICE "MICKEY MOUSE"...

"GROCER'S DAUGHTER SHALL NOT EVER HAVE THE CASH OF SOUTH WALES MINERS!" GROCER'S DAUGHTER CALLED ACCOUNTANTS FIRM OF 'POODLE SLAUGHTERHOUSE'

POODLE SLAUGHTERHOUSE GOT WORKING ON THE FUNDS OF SOUTH WALES MINERS...

TOOK THE CASH FROM THOSE WHOSE WILFUL DISREGARD OF ALL THINGS LAWFUL....

MADE IT RIGHT THAT THEY SHOULD FORFEIT ALL DOWN TO THEIR UNDERWEAR....

GAVE THE CASH FOR MINERS' CHILDREN TO TWO GLOUCESTER MILLIONAIRES....

34

35

VIRGO
August 22nd-September 22nd

You're sweet fresh and innocent and you've never had it so good. Bank Holiday brings a welcome break for many of you, but beware of Druids with sharp knives.

**Some well known Virgos
Cecil Parkinson
Denis Healey**

37

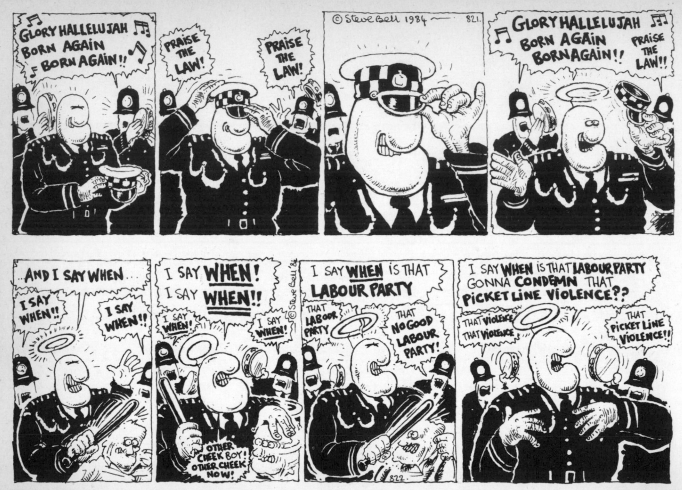

39

41

42

43

LIBRA
September 23rd-October 22nd

Unbalanced Libras have a tendency to clank alarmingly. The equinox means that Father Christmas is rising, so watch out for bargains, especially when Pluto is in Disneyland.

Some well known Librans
Margaret Thatcher
Leon Brittan

49

50

51

52

57

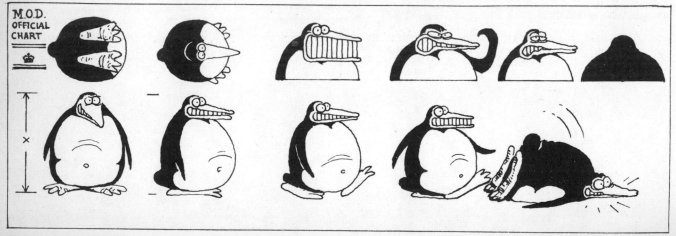

59

61

PENGUIN PRESENTATION BEHAVIOUR (ANTARCTIC SPRING)

62

SCORPIO
October 23rd-November 22nd

You're a little shiny crawler with a lethal poisoned sting in your tail, but inside you have a heart of gold.

Some of you may feel the need to burn effigies around the fifth of the month.

Don't let people tread on you.

Some well known Scorpios
Roy Jenkins
Kenneth Baker

63

65

67

HO·O·OME HO·O·OME ON THE R·A·A·A·A·NGE....
WHEEEE
...WHERE THE... GORDON BENNETT!!
BLAM
© Steve Bell 1984
878
YOU TROD ON AN ARGIE MINE – IT'S PART OF A CONCERTED ATTACK ON DEMOCRACY!
BUT THAT WAS A BRITISH SHELL NOT AN ARGIE MINE!
I BEG YOUR PARDON – –IT'S PART OF A CONCERTED DEFENCE AGAINST TYRANNY. BUT DON'T WORRY – I GUARANTEE YOU'LL BE AT LEAST NINE PERCENT MORE POPULAR NOW THAN YOU WERE BEFORE!!

LARRY'S JUST HAD A MIRACULOUS ESCAPE!
PRAISE BE!
YOU WILL BE PLEASED TO HEAR THAT HE HAS DECIDED TO ENTER POLITICS...
GOOD LORD!
GREAT SCOTT!
...ON BEHALF OF THE WAR PARTY!
HE'S CERTAINLY GOT MY VOTE!
..AND MINE!
© Steve Bell 1984
879.
I'M RENOUNCING WOOLLY-MINDED SOCIALISM FOREVER!!
ME TOO!
ME TOO!
AND ME!

70

MEANWHILE, BACK IN THE U.K.:
HEY- -DUTCH ELM!! I WANNA WORD WITH YOU!!
JUST A MINUTE BOSS— I'M THINKING...
HMMM- -I NEED TO GO TO THE TOILET
SNAP
ELDERLY Mac
DUTCH ELM
...BUT I'D BETTER TAKE A BALLOT ON IT, JUST TO MAKE SURE...
"ALL THOSE IN FAVOUR OF GOING TO THE TOILET RAISE THEIR HANDS..!"
C'MON— HURRY IT UP WILLYA!?
"ALL THOSE AGAINST?"
WELL, IT LOOKS LIKE IT'S UNANIMOUS- -I'M GOING TO THE TOILET.
YOU'RE TAKIN' YOUR TIME FELLA!!
OOPS... TOO LATE!!
JUST WHAT IN HELL DO YOU THINK YOU'RE DOIN' DUTCHELM?
© Steve Bell 1984
882.

I'M GONNA CONFIDE SOMETHING IN YOU, DUTCH ELM-YOU CAN KEEP A SECRET CAN'T YOU?
YES BOSS
ELDERLY Mac
DUTCH ELM
883.
...I'M GONNA LEAVE THIS GODDAMN COUNTRY VERY SHORTLY, AND I STRONGLY ADVISE YOU TO DO THE SAME....
YES BOSS?
DUTCH ELM
...THE WHOLE GODDAMN PLACE IS SHOT THROUGH WITH GOD- -DAMN COMMIES — THE GODDAMN COALBOARD IS FULLA' COMMIES! I'M GOIN' BACK TO WHERE A MAN CAN WIELD A HATCHET IN AN ATMOSPHERE OF TRUE FREEDOM!
© Steve Bell 1984
YOU'RE GOIN' BACK TO AMERICA THEN, BOSS?
NO, I'M GOIN' RIGHT BACK HOME TO URANUS!
ELDERLY MAC

74

SAGITTARIUS
November 23rd-December 20th

Half human half bull, you enjoy 'The Archers' but sympathise with the animals.

If you don't put your shirts on some of you will get very cold this month.

Some well known Sagittarians
Sir Geoffrey Howe
John Selwyn Gummer

80

83

84

86

CAPRICORN
December 21st-January 19th

You're the sort of person who will eat anything, but lay off the tin cans and rubber tyres if you want to avoid stomach trouble. You may find some cause for celebration towards the end of the month.

Some well known Capricorns
Sir Keith Joseph
Roy Hattersley
Jesus Christ

90

A POST-PRANDIAL FAMILY ENCOUNTER GROUP SOMEWHERE IN ENGLAND:
I KNOW WHAT, CHAPS—LET'S PLAY A GAME!
A GAME?? LEAVE IT ITE, CHARLES!
916
NO—I'M SERIOUS——I'VE GOT THIS BRAND NEW ELECTRONIC GAME TO HELP US CONQUER OUR INHIBITIONS!
I'M NOT TAKING ORFF MY TRIZERS FOR ANYONE!
OH REALLY CHARLES!!
NODDINGTONS CULTURE SHOCK FOR THE FAMILY THAT HAS EVERYTHING
OKAY—NOW EVERYBODY PUTS A FUNNY HAT ON, I PUSH THE BUTTON, AND THE NEW HI-TECH, STATE-OF-THE-ART ELECTRONICS TAKE OVER!!
SILLY BLOODY NONSENSE!
© Steve Bell 1984
'ERE—WOSSER GAME? I'VE COME OVER ALL LOWER CLASS!!
STUFF THIS—I'M OFF AHT TO BLOW AWAY A FEW TWEETERS!
THASSALL YOU THINK ABAHT, INNIT? ANY EXCUSE TO DO OVER A BIT O'WILDLIFE!
'ERE—THE BABY'S DONE A MOBY ONNA CARPET!!

A WELL KNOWN FAMILY ARE PLAYING 'CULTURE SHOCK':
—'ERE BONE 'EAD—I CAN'T FIND THE NUTCRACKERS—NUT THIS BRAZIL NUT OPEN FOR ME, WOODGER??
RIGHTCHAR GIRL!
917
GOR—YOU GOT CLASS, BONE'EAD!
AHZAT!?
ADZEE DO IT??
I'LL TELL YOU GIRL—IT TOOK CENTURIES O'BREEDIN' TO GET MY BONCE INTO THIS CONDITION!
GOR—THAT BRAZIL NUT'S WELL BUGGERED!
PONK
DID SOMEBODY MENTION BREEDING? WHERE? WHERE??
RANDY ANDY!—YOUR MUVVER'S GOT A FEW WORDS TO SAY TO YOU, BOY!!
YEAH—I'LL TELL YOU SOMETHIN', BOY—YOU TIE A KNOT IN IT WHILE YOU'RE UNDER OUR ROOF, YOU GET MY DRIFT?
© Steve Bell 1984

91

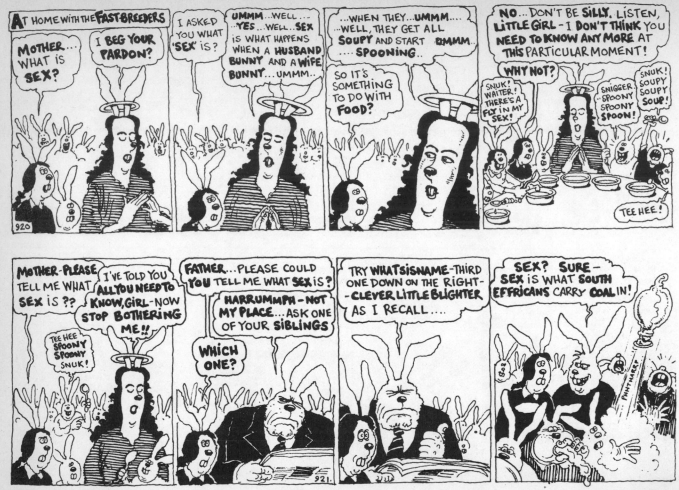

94

AQUARIUS
January 20th-February 18th

Modern plumbing technology
has made the Water Carrier a
thing of the past, with the
result that many Aquarians
are finding themselves
without work at the moment.

Some of you may also be
feeling the cold this month.

Some well known Aquarians
Francis Pym
Norman Fowler
Ronald Reagan

101

105

106

108

110

PISCES
February 19th-March 20th

You're cold, slimy and difficult to pin down, but don't let this worry you as you're also extremely good to eat.

Some Pisceans will be getting tired of the cold weather.

Your finances need care.

Some well known Pisceans
Sir Michael Havers
Nigel Lawson
Randy Andy

111

115

116

117

118

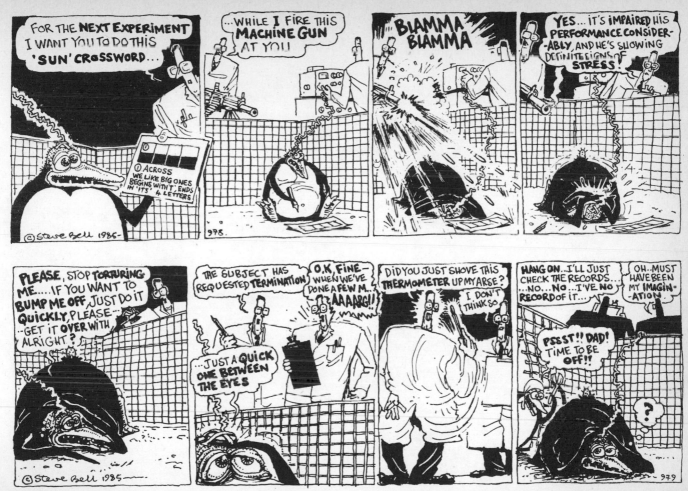

123

ARIES
March 21st-April 20th

You're stubborn and woolly, but you like the occasional dip. Watch out for people taking the piss round about the 1st.

Outlook: fairly rammy.

Some well known Arians
Michael Heseltine
Norman Tebbit
Peter Walker
James Callaghan
Neil Kinnock
Tony Benn
Ian Paisley
Julian Amery
Adolf Hitler
Genghis Khan
Emperor Nero
The Devil
The Borgias
Bambi
Pontius Pilate
David Steel

125

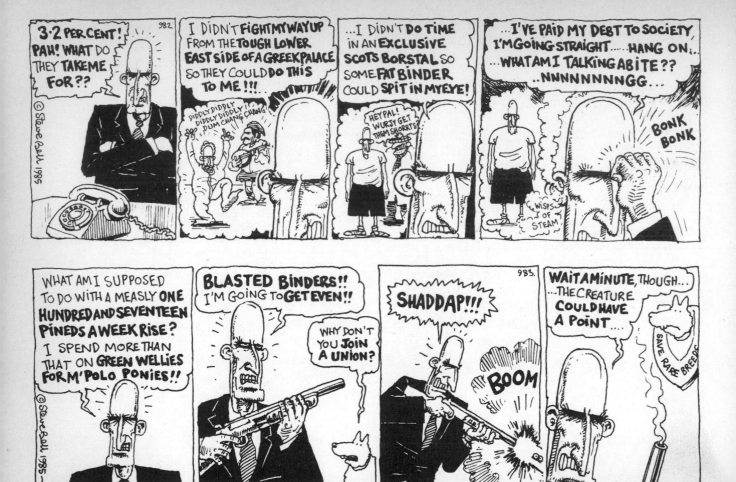

129

131

TAURUS
April 21st-May 20th

Taureans have a tendency to be full of bullshit, but on the positive side you look great with a ring through your nose.

It's important that you keep away from Spaniards in funny hats.

Some well known Taureans
H.M. The Queen (Unofficially)
Norman St John Stevas

139

141

142

143

144

145

147

148

GEMINI
May 21st-June 20th

Those born under this sign tend to be four-eyed two-faced schizophrenics. Try not to worry about this, remember it takes two to tango, but only one in your case.

Some of the wealthier among you may have official birthdays this month.

Some well known Geminis
Rhodes Boyson
Enoch Powell
H.M. The Queen (Officially)
The Duke of Edinburgh
(Unofficially)

154

158

Russell Orsiz